the..
Eggcellent
EGG fun
book

the.. Eggcellent EGG fun book

Peter Eldin

Illustrated by Ant Parker

Hippo Books
Scholastic Children's Books
London

Scholastic Children's Books,
Scholastic Publications Ltd,
7-9 Pratt Street, London NW1 0AE, UK

Scholastic Inc.,
730 Broadway, New York, NY 10003, USA

Scholastic Canada Ltd,
123 Newkirk Road, Richmond Hill,
Ontario, Canada L4C 3G5

Ashton Scholastic Pty Ltd,
PO Box 579, Gosford, New South Wales,
Australia

Ashton Scholastic Ltd,
Private Bag 1, Penrose, Auckland 6,
New Zealand

Text copyright © Peter Eldin, 1992

Illustrations copyright © Ant Parker, 1992

ISBN 0 590 55100 0

Printed and bound in Great Britain by
Cox & Wyman Ltd, Reading, Berkshire

CONTENTS

An egg is an extraordinary thing! It's designed to be strong from the outside, but weak from the inside. This means that it can be protected from any outside pressure that might cause it to break, but it is still easy for the baby inside to break through the shell.

An egg is incredibly strong! Hold a hen's egg in the middle, between your thumb and forefinger, and squeeze. You will break the egg – and get a gooey hand! This might make you think that eggs will always break easily.

But, now, take another egg and hold it lengthways. You'll find it much more difficult to crush because the design of the egg makes it strong.

The egg is smaller at one end than at the other, so that it won't roll around in the nest. The eggs in a bird's nest will normally be pointing inwards. This way, if there are several eggs in the nest they take up less room.

Did you know....?

Eggs contain over fifty chemicals and organic substances. These include calcium, sugar, iodine, fat, zinc, fluorine, lead, magnesium sulphur, chromium, copper, aluminium and silver!

ALL SORTS OF EGGS

Eggs range in size from tiny ones laid by insects and fish, to huge ostrich eggs.

We usually imagine that only birds lay eggs, but in fact many other creatures do too. In fact, all animal life comes from an egg, but in many animals the eggs are inside the body instead of outside.

Dinosaurs laid eggs. Many fossilized dinosaur eggs have been found, but for a long time people didn't realize what they were. The first dinosaur eggs were identified in 1922, when a whole nest was discovered in the Gobi Desert in Mongolia.

The largest egg ever laid was probably that of the Madagascar Elephant Bird, which is now extinct. The egg would have been twice the size of an ostrich egg!

Of course, you will only need to use hens' eggs for the activities in this book, although other birds' eggs are available in shops. Ducks' eggs are quite common, for example. They are larger and have a richer taste than hens' eggs, but they need to be eaten when fresh. Goose eggs are larger still, but they taste much the same as a duck's egg.

You can eat fish eggs too, in the form of caviar. They are tiny, black, extremely expensive, and you probably won't even like the taste, so they are best avoided!

From a cook's point of view, eggs are extremely important. They can be served in all sorts of ways and are a basic ingredient for lots of recipes.

INSIDE AN EGG

The shell protects the baby inside the egg and stops germs from getting in. It also stops too much water escaping from the egg. This keeps the insides in good condition.

The membrane is a fine skin.

The vitelline membrane holds the yolk together.

Air pocket An egg slowly loses water. As it does so, this air pocket gets bigger to take up the space. The smaller the air pocket the fresher the egg.
Next time you peel the shell from a hard-boiled egg, look to see how big the air pocket was.

The yolk is full of goodness, as it contains food for the baby that would develop if the egg was fertilized.

The albumen is usually known as the "white" of the egg. If you break open an egg you will see that there are two types of white. One is thicker than the other.

The egg cell is the part of the egg which would have developed into the baby if the egg had been fertilized.

The chalazae are twisted strands of membrane that hold the yolk in the middle of the egg.

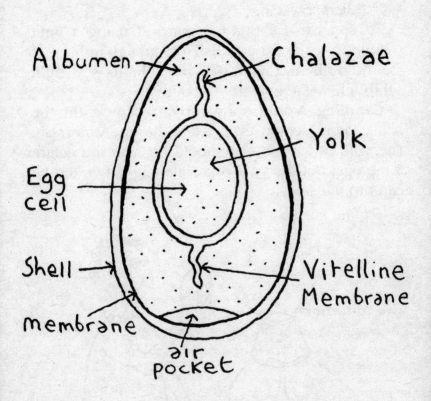

Albumen

Chalazae

Yolk

Egg cell

Shell

Vitelline Membrane

membrane

air pocket

Did you know...?

The shell of a hen's egg is about 0.32 mm thick. But the thickness varies from season to season and according to the chicken's health and diet.

SEE-THROUGH EGGS

Years ago, people used to hold a candle behind an egg to see if it was fresh. This was called "candling".

You can try this for yourself using a light bulb instead of a candle. Hold an egg in front of a lit bulb and you will be able to see right through it (the egg, not the bulb!).

Candling would show up any cracks in the shell. People could even tell if the egg was fresh. The yolk of a fresh egg should be near the centre of the egg, but the yolk of a stale egg may often be nearer to the side.

EGGS to EAT

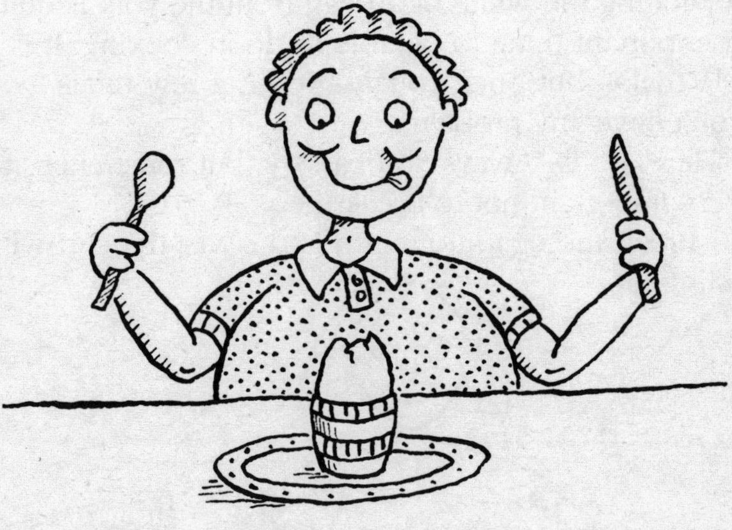

There are six easy ways to cook eggs.

They can be boiled, fried, baked, poached, scrambled or made into an omelette.

You can try each of these methods for yourself but always let an adult know if you're planning to do any cooking.

Did you know...?

If you take eggs from the fridge 20 to 30 minutes before cooking, they will taste even better!

Separate an egg

Separating the white of an egg from the yolk is quite an important thing to be able to do in cooking. It is a little tricky, but once you've tried it a few times, you won't have any problems.

Here are two ways you can try, but remember, it's very important not to break the yolk.

1. Break the egg into a cup and cover the cup with cling film.

2. Make a small slit in the cling film.
3. Holding the cup over a small bowl, gently tip it upside down and the egg white will pour into the bowl, whilst the yolk stays in the cup.

When you're really practised you can have a go at the second method:
1. Hold the egg over a bowl and break it gently.
2. Tip the egg so that the yolk and the white are in one half of the shell.

3. Now carefully tip the yolk into the other half shell. As you do this, the white will slide into the bowl beneath the egg.
4. Keep tipping the yolk backwards and forwards until all (or most) of the white is in the bowl.

BOILED EGGS

Cooking is fun and quite easy provided that you take care. Start out by boiling some eggs, then have a go at some more adventurous recipes in this book.

1. Use a small saucepan and put in just enough water to cover the egg.

2. Put the saucepan of water on the gas or electric ring and bring it to the boil.

3. Use a large spoon to lower the egg gently into the water.

An average-sized egg will take about 3 minutes to cook so that it is soft-boiled and 5 minutes until it is hard-boiled.

If you want to eat a cold hard-boiled egg, boil it for longer – up to ten minutes for best results.

To stop the shell cracking when boiling
an egg try one of these tips:
1. Put the egg into cold water and time it
from the point that the water starts to boil.
2. Prick the blunt end of the egg with a pin
before boiling.
3. Put a few drops of vinegar into the water.

If the shell cracks while your egg is boiling,
sprinkle a little salt on the crack to stop the insides
from seeping out.

If you put hard-boiled eggs into cold water they
will stop cooking. This makes it easier to get the
shells off too. It also stops a black line forming
between the white and the yolk. The line won't harm
you, but it doesn't look very nice!

Did you know...?
An old custom was always to turn the shell of a
boiled egg upside down in the egg cup once it
was eaten. The end was then smashed, to make
sure there would be plenty more eggs to eat!

SCRAMBLED EGGS

You will need for each person:

2 eggs
2 tablespoons (30ml) milk
15g/½ oz butter
salt and pepper

1. Break the eggs into a bowl, add the milk and then beat them with a fork. Stir in a little salt and pepper.

2. Put the butter in a saucepan and heat it gently until the butter begins to melt. Carefully pour in the egg and keep stirring until the mixture begins to thicken.

3. Take the pan off the heat but keep stirring until the eggs become fluffy.

4. Spoon them out onto the plate or onto a slice of hot buttered toast.

MORE SCRAMBLES

Now you can make scrambled eggs, have a go at some of these versions too.

1. Mix in some pieces of chopped ham just before you serve the eggs.

2. Mix in some grated cheese just after you take the eggs from the heat.

3. Add some finely chopped spring onions to ready cooked eggs.

4. Sprinkle some chopped fresh parsley over the eggs before serving.

5. For a real "eggstravaganza", you could try putting all of these ideas together!

POACHED EGGS

Most people poach eggs in a cup or a special poaching holder immersed in water. In fact this is not poaching at all – it is steaming.

1. The correct way to poach an egg is to put about 4cm (1½ in) of water into a frying pan. Add some salt and then bring it to simmering point (this is just before it starts boiling).

2. Break the egg into a cup and then slide it into the water.

3. Cook it in the water for 2 to 3 minutes.

Did you know...?

Over twelve thousand million eggs are eaten in the British Isles every year. That's about 225 eggs to each person!

STUFFED EGGS

Stuffed eggs are brilliant for parties!

1. Hard boil some eggs (see p.18), say one or two per person.
2. Leave them to cool then peel off the shells.
3. Cut each egg in half and scoop out the yolk.
4. Mix the yolks with any of the suggested stuffing mixes below and then pile the mixture back into the whites.
5. Decorate each half egg with one of the toppings below.

You don't have to stick to the suggestions listed. You can mix the yolks with anything you like but try them yourself first before you make them for your friends.

stuffing mix	**topping**
sardines	parsley
grated cheese	slice of pepper
cream cheese	tomato
pâté	chopped nuts
mayonnaise	cayenne pepper
tuna	salami
chopped ham	chopped spring onion

TOADSTOOLS

Hang on a minute! What are toadstools doing in a book about eggs? Well, actually, these toadstools are made with eggs and, unlike real toadstools, these are made for eating! This is how you do it:

To make 4 toadstools you will need:

4 eggs   2 tomatoes
cress   1 tube cream cheese

1. First boil four eggs (see p.18).
2. Let the eggs cool down, then peel off the shells.

Pooh!

3. Cut a small slice from the top and bottom of each egg. (You can eat these bits now, if you like – that's one of the nice bits about being a **cook!**).

4. Cut the two tomatoes in half.

5. Cover a plate with cress.

6. Stand the four eggs on the plate. Balance half a tomato on top of each egg.

7. Use the tube of cream cheese to put little dots over the tomatoes so they look like the markings on toadstools. If you cannot find a tube of cheese, use a skewer or a knitting needle to put the spots on from an ordinary tub of cream cheese.

POTATO SURPRISE

Potato Surprise is easy to make and it's really tasty.

For four people you will need:

4 medium-sized potatoes, cleaned

4 eggs

50g (2 oz) cheddar cheese, grated

15g (½ oz) butter

2 tablespoons (30 ml) milk

Salt and pepper

1. Preheat the oven to 220°C/425°F/gas mark 7.
2. Make a cross cut in the top of each potato and then bake them in the oven for about an hour.

3. Allow the potatoes to cool and then spoon out the insides into a bowl.
4. Mash the insides of the potato with the milk, butter, cheese and a little salt and pepper.

5. Half fill each potato with the mixture.
There should be some left over.
6. Carefully break an egg into each potato.

7. Put the potatoes back into the oven at 180°C/350°F/gas mark 4 for fifteen minutes.
8. Take the potatoes out of the oven and carefully fill each one with the remaining potato/cheese mixture. Put them under the grill until they brown. Watch them carefully!

Don't tell your friends what's in the middle. Let them discover the "surprise" for themselves!

SUGAR EGGS

To make about twelve sugar eggs you will need:

225 g (8 oz) caster sugar

food colouring

1 egg white (see p.16)

1. Put the caster sugar in a bowl.

2. Add two or three drops of food colouring. You don't need very much!

3. Mix in the egg white.

4. Take a lump of the mixture and press it between two teaspoons into an egg shape.

5. Put the egg on a piece of kitchen towel to dry.

6. Make three more eggs like this.

7. Add a couple more drops of food colouring to the mixture in the bowl.

8. Repeat steps 4 to 7 until all the mixture has been used up.

9. You will now have about a dozen very tasty looking eggs!

You could make different-coloured eggs too. Separate the mixture into two or three small bowls, and add a different colour to each bowl.

Don't eat your eggs until they are dry!

CHOCOLATE EASTER EGGS

Most people would probably agree that the nicest egg you can eat is a chocolate one. Did you know you can make them yourself?

Ideally, you will need a special plastic mould, which you can buy from a kitchen shop or the kitchen section of a department store. They are available in lots of different sizes.

For a large mould you will need about 225g/8oz melted cooking chocolate (available in most supermarkets).

1. Break the chocolate into pieces and put it in a heat-proof bowl.

2. Ask an adult to give you a hand to melt the chocolate, as it can be quite a tricky process. Rest the bowl on top of a pan of hot water, and heat the pan gently, so that the water simmers.

3. Keep heating the chocolate over the water, and stir gently with a wooden spoon until it has all melted and the mixture is shiny and smooth.

4. Allow the chocolate to cool slightly.

5. Use a clean pastry brush to coat the inside of each mould with a thick layer of chocolate. (If you don't have a brush, pour a couple of tablespoons of melted chocolate into the mould and tip the mould around so the chocolate spreads evenly all over the inside.)

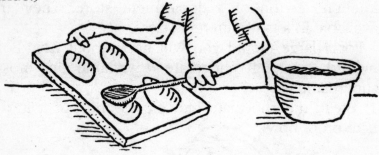

6. Put the moulds open-side down on some greaseproof paper. Leave them to set.

7. Once the moulds are set, add a little more melted chocolate in the same way, to make a thicker layer. The larger the mould you use, the thicker the chocolate needs to be.

8. Put the moulds in the ice compartment of the fridge for ten minutes.

9. Take them out of the fridge and give them a sharp tap. The moulded chocolate should come out quite easily. If it doesn't, pop the moulds back in the fridge for a few more minutes, then try again.

10. Fill the eggs with sweets or a small gift to give as a present, but don't finger them too much, they may melt!

11. To stick 2 halves together, use a little melted chocolate and brush it around the join. You may need to smooth over the join with a knife.

12. Add a ribbon or bow as a smart finishing touch.

Alternatively, you could make your own moulds from a plastic egg carton.

It may be easier to make a solid egg this way, by pouring melted chocolate into the mould until it is full. Join two half eggs together by spreading chocolate in the middle.

CHEESY EGGS

Here's a simple but very tasty snack for four people.

You will need:

4 eggs
40 g (1½ oz) butter or margarine
2 tablespoons grated cheese
salt and pepper

1. Set the oven at 200°C/400°F/gas mark 6.
2. Grease the insides of 4 small dishes (a bun tray would be ideal for this) with butter or margarine.
3. Put some of the cheese into each dish, leaving half for later.
4. Break an egg into each dish.
5. Sprinkle some salt and pepper on top of each egg.
6. Add the rest of the cheese.
7. Pop a blob of butter on top of each egg.
8. Bake the eggs in the oven for about 10 minutes.
9. When the eggs are cooked, tip each one onto a slice of hot toast and serve immediately.

RAW OR HARD BOILED?

How can you tell whether an egg is raw or hard boiled without breaking it?

Carefully spin the egg on its pointed end,
A raw egg will fall over straight away.
A hard–boiled egg will spin!

UNDERGROUND EGGS

The Chinese like buried eggs. They bury them in salt and wet clay or ashes for a month! Or they bury them in salt and boiled rice for six months.

But to the real expert, eggs buried for fifty years in lime, salt, ashes and tea are said to be the best!

34

Did you know...?
The hens whose eggs we eat today have developed from wild jungle birds of the Far East. Farmers first began keeping them for their eggs about four thousand years ago!

EGGSTRA-ORDINARY facts about eggs...

THE PANCAKE GREAZE

The Pancake Greaze is an old custom of Westminster School in London. Each Shrove Tuesday the school cook and the verger carry an omelette to a high iron bar that separates the Lower and Upper Schools.

The cook tosses the pancake over the bar and the boys scramble to catch a piece. The boy who gets the biggest piece of omelette is awarded a golden guinea.

Unfortunately, he has to give the guinea back immediately but he does get some extra pocket money to spend.

THE PANCAKE RACE

On Shrove Tuesday every year, a pancake race is held in Olney in Buckinghamshire that has become famous all over the world! The race is thought to date back to 1450.

Only women are allowed to enter. To qualify, they must live in Olney and they need to wear a skirt, apron and hat and carry a pancake in a frying pan when they take part. The women race 380 m (400 yds) to the local church, tossing their pancakes as they run!

Shrove Tuesday is the last day before Lent. Lent lasts for 40 days and is traditionally a time for fasting. Pancakes were originally made before Lent as a way of using up rich foods, such as butter, milk and eggs, before the fasting began.

EGGSTREMELY LARGE!

About a hundred years ago, the firm of Buszards in Oxford Street, London, made a chocolate Easter egg that was 2.75 m (9 feet) high and measured 5.5 m (18 feet) around the middle. Even when empty, it took seven men to carry it on a specially made stretcher. It was made to carry the trousseau for a millionaire's bride and many of the wedding presents as well!

In Victorian times a certain young man sent his lady friend a gigantic Easter egg. When it was broken open out came two ponies pulling a magnificent carriage!

Did you know...?
The British spend over £134,000,000 on chocolate Easter eggs each year!

EGG ROLLS

In Preston, Lancashire, hard-boiled eggs
are rolled down a hill on Easter Monday.
Any that are damaged are shelled and eaten.

Egg rolling also takes place in Central Park,
New York and on the lawns of the White House,
in Washington, home of the American President.

GREEN EGGS FOR BREAKFAST

In southern France, in 1974, hens started to lay
green eggs! No-one knew why, so the farmers
decided to investigate. The reason, they found, was
a plague of crickets! The crickets were so plentiful
that the hens gobbled them as fast as they could.
Colouring in the body of the crickets was
transferred into the hens' eggs and made them
green as well!

SECRET MESSAGES

During the First World War, French resistance fighters sometimes carried secret messages in eggs.

The message was written on the outside of the shell, using a brush dipped in a solution of one ounce of alum to one pint of vinegar.

When the message dried it was completely invisible.

When the egg was boiled the writing was still invisible.

But, when the shell was peeled from the boiled egg the writing could be seen on the white of the egg!

EGGS CAN MAKE YOU BEAUTIFUL!

If you would like your hair to be shiny rub a beaten egg into it.

Comb the egg through your hair and then leave it for about 15 minutes.

Now rinse off the egg making sure the water isn't too hot!

Eggs can be used for a soothing cream for sunburn.

You will need:

1 egg white
1 teaspoon of honey
½ teaspoon of witch hazel

Blend the ingredients together to make a smooth paste.

Put it on any sunburnt areas of skin and you'll find it feels much better!

Keep in the fridge but don't try to eat it!

VEAL AND HAM SECRET

Cut a slice of traditional English veal and ham pie, and you'll always find a circle of boiled egg in each slice.

How come it's the same width all the way through? you wonder.

The answer is, that, through the process invented 35 years ago, whites and yolks of the eggs are separated. The yolk is poured into a long cylinder and the white is made into a tube to surround the yolk. This is held together in a long, thin case which is removed once the pie has been cooked!

Did you know...?
Snails eggs are very popular in some high class restaurants. Apparently they have a slight almond taste.

EASTER EGGS AND RABBITS

Our word Easter comes from the name of the goddess of spring, Eostre.

According to legend, she owned a beautiful pet bird. One day, in a fit of anger she used her magic powers and changed the bird into a rabbit. On the first day of spring, the rabbit, thinking of its life as a bird, built a nest and filled it with eggs.

As a result, rabbits and eggs are now a traditional part of Easter celebrations in many parts of the world.

In France, children are told that rabbits and hares travel to Rome at Easter to collect eggs. German children are told that hares actually lay the Easter eggs.

Children in Finland make small nests, fill them with stones and hide them around the house. On Maundy Thursday, everyone is blindfolded and they set about searching for the nests.

Many people around the world believe that an egg boiled at Easter will never go bad.

THE REAL HUMPTY

Humpty Dumpty sat on a wall
Humpty Dumpty had a great fall
All the king's horses
And all the king's men
Couldn't put Humpty together again.

Pictures used to illustrate this famous nursery rhyme always show Humpty Dumpty as an egg-shaped character. But, in fact, Humpty Dumpty had nothing to do with eggs. The connection is, that eggs break easily and cannot be repaired. The real Humpty Dumpty wasn't even a person. Humpty Dumpty was a machine!

According to one story it was used during the Civil War, which took place in England over three hundred years ago. King Charles I's army planned

to attack a castle, but to get to it, they had to cross a wide river. As men could be drowned in the crossing, a special wheeled machine was built to carry them across. The machine, called Humpty Dumpty, would be rolled down the hill towards the river. When it reached the water it would be travelling so fast that it would roll straight across the surface of the river, carrying the soldiers with it.

The machine was made and rolled down the hill. But all did not go according to plan. Humpty Dumpty crashed in the middle of the river. Many soldiers were drowned and Humpty Dumpty had broken into so many pieces, that "all the king's horses and all the king's men couldn't put Humpty together again".

FABULOUS FABERGÉ EGGS

In 1883 the Tsarina of Russia was feeling a little sad, so Tsar Alexander III decided to give her a special present for Easter. It was a fabulous egg of pure gold, made by the French jeweller Carl Fabergé.

Inside the egg was a golden yolk...inside the yolk was a small hen with ruby eyes...inside the hen was a miniature version of the imperial crown...and inside the crown was a ruby pendant.

The Tsarina was so pleased with her present that the Tsar ordered Fabergé to make one every year, and the tradition carried on for many years after Alexander III's death.

In 1987 a balloon company made a hot air balloon in the shape of an egg. It was a replica of one of the Fabergé eggs. The Fabergé egg is 6.5 cm (2½ in) high, but the balloon had a height of 27.5 m (90 feet)!

EGGS AT THE OPERA

The great opera star, Enrico Caruso, once became very annoyed because a soprano was getting more attention than him on stage. She did this by over-acting and continually clasping her hands together dramatically. One night, during her main aria, she was just about to clasp her hands together, when Caruso slipped an egg between her hands. The egg cracked, dripped down her hands and dress, and the audience screamed with laughter.

Did you know...?
An egg was once dropped 198 m (650 feet) from a helicopter onto a golf course in Tokyo, Japan...and it didn't break!

Did you know ...?
Augustus Leopold Egg was a British artist who lived about 150 years ago. His most famous painting was called, "Queen Elizabeth discovers she is no longer young".

COLOUR AN EGG

Why not try out one of the oldest Easter traditions this year, and make a pace egg?

The word "pace" come from "pesach", a Greek word for "Passover". The egg is a symbol of new life and, colouring and eating eggs was a custom of the spring festival, which later became an Easter tradition.

Years ago, people made yellow pace eggs by wrapping an ordinary egg in onion skin (tied in place with a piece of clean cloth, or by wrapping cotton around the egg). It was then boiled in the normal way. When the egg was unwrapped it had a yellow, marbled pattern all over it!

Other traditional ways of decorating an egg included:

  wrapping strands of grass or fern around the egg before boiling it, to make an unusual pattern on the shell;

  boiling it in coffee or tea to turn the shell brown;

  wrapping it in spinach or cabbage leaves to colour it green;

  boiling it in water that has been used to cook beetroot to turn the shell red.

  Of course, if you want to cheat, you could just add food colouring to the water you boil the egg in and make all sorts of coloured eggs!

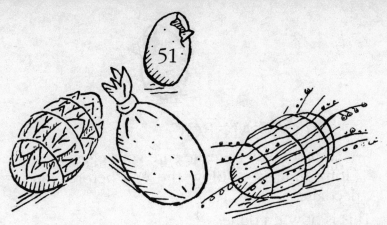

If you plan to eat the egg then you need to boil it only for about five minutes (see p.18). But an ordinary boiled egg won't last very long and should be eaten within a day of cooking. If you want your egg to last longer and don't intend eating it, you should let it simmer in the pan for at least half an hour so the inside will get really hard.

Did you know...?
In 1307 King Edward I of England ordered 450 eggs to be boiled, dyed and decorated for his servants at Easter.

BLOW AN EGG

Another way to make sure your eggs last a long time is to blow the egg before you decorate it.

This is how it's done:

1. Don't use an egg straight from the fridge. It's best at, roughly, room temperature.

2. Use a hat pin or the point of a safety pin to pierce a small hole in the wider end of the egg.

3. If you find it difficult to push the pin in you can tap it gently with a wooden spoon. Better still, ask an adult to do it for you.

4. Make another hole in the other end of the egg. Use the pin to make this hole bigger than the first.

5. Push the pin right into the egg, through one of the holes you have just made. This will break the yolk.

6. Hold the egg with your thumb over the big hole and your forefinger over the other hole. Shake it to mix the yolk and the white together.

7. Now, hold the egg over a bowl and blow through the small hole, using a straw, forcing the contents out through the other end and into the bowl.

(Don't throw the contents away, you can still use them to make scrambled egg (see p.20) or omelettes. But don't wait for more than a day before you use it).

8. Rinse out the egg shell under a running tap.

9. Rinse it again in a bowl of warm water with a few drops of washing up liquid in it. This will stop the shell from smelling.

10. Place it upright on a paper towel, a newspaper, or in an egg box until it has dried out completely.

11. Use plaster filler, wood filler or tissue paper to fill in the holes at each end of the egg.

12. Now turn to page 54 and start decorating.

PAINT AN EGG

Of course, you can paint an Easter egg with any design you like!

Try painting faces. See if you can make them look like members of your family, or friends. Or paint a clown's face.

You can use felt-tipped pens, crayons or poster paints. But if you are using a hard-boiled egg and want to eat it later, don't use household dyes or poster paints – they could make you very ill.

If you are using a blown egg, put a layer of clear varnish all over it once you've decorated it – this will protect your masterpiece!

Did you know...?
To make sure no-one else uses the same facial design, clowns paint a copy of their make-up on an egg.

HOLDING THE EGG

One of the problems with painting eggs is keeping your fingers out of the way!

The pictures on this page show some ideas for holding the egg upright so you can paint the egg without having to hold it

1. Put the egg in an egg cup or an egg box. Paint the top half of the egg. When the paint has dried, turn the egg over and then paint the other half.

2. Make a small "nest" with Plasticine or dough to support the egg.

3. Thread a piece of cotton through the egg. Tie some knots in the cotton to stop the egg slipping off. Hang it up. This method is only really suitable for blown eggs. You have to be careful that the egg doesn't move too much while you're painting.

4. Support the egg on a candle stick or the neck of a bottle.

5. Support the egg on the cardboard inner tube from a roll of sticky tape or the cap from a small bottle.

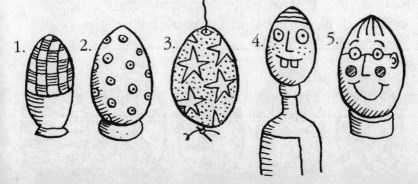

EASTER DECORATIONS

There are all sorts of ways you can decorate your eggs. Have a go at some of these, then see if you can think of some ideas of your own.

1. Cut out patterns and pictures from comics and magazines and stick them on the egg.

2. Glue sequins on the shell.

3. Put some glue on the shell and sprinkle it with glitter from a tube.

4. Glue dried lentils, melon seeds, apple pips, beads or anything else you can think of on the shell.

5. Use water to stick some fern leaves on the shell. Use a spray paint to colour the egg then take the ferns away. You will be left with a leafy pattern.

6. Use nail varnish instead of paint to decorate your eggs. If you use different colours leave each colour to dry before putting on another one.

7. Dip an old piece of sponge into paint and dab it on the egg shell.

8. Coat the egg in glue and then wrap different coloured wools around it. You can do this with several different colours.

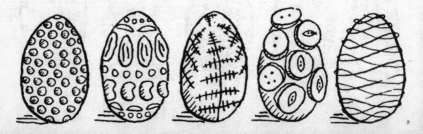

EGG TREE

To make an egg tree you will need:
　some blown, decorated eggs,
　some twigs,
　cotton,
　ribbons of different colours,
　a deep bowl,
　a large lump of Plasticine or a piece of Oasis
　(a green, spongy material used for flower
　arranging)

1. Put the Plasticine (or Oasis) in the bottom of your bowl.
2. Stand the twigs in the Plasticine.
3. Fix the ribbons to the egg by pushing the end into one of the holes made for blowing and then sealing it with plaster filler or Plasticine.
4. Hook the ribbons onto the twigs by making a loop with the cotton.
5. Put the finished egg tree on a table or a windowsill.

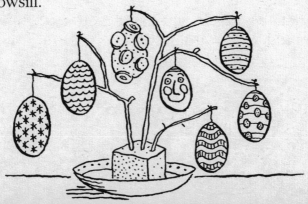

Did you know...?

In China, when a new baby is born, people paint eggs red to give as presents. These are believed to bring good luck to the baby.

EGGSTRA-VAGANZA

of magic tricks and

GAMES

HOW TO YARP

Yarping (or "jarping") is a game enjoyed in the north of England at Eastertime. In some places it's also called "shackling".

The idea is to knock your egg against your friend's egg. If your friend's egg cracks you win and you take the egg as your prize.

This game is played in other countries too. In Greece they knock red dyed eggs together and the person whose egg cracks last is said to have good luck.

Some people say that adding a little vinegar to the water you boil your egg in will strengthen its shell. But that would be cheating, wouldn't it?

IMPOSSIBLE BALANCE

To make this amazing balancing egg you first need a blown egg. See page 52 for instructions on how to do this.

1. Make sure your egg is completely dry.

2. Seal up the smaller of the two holes in the egg with plaster filler or tissue paper.

3. Use a small spoon to pour some salt carefully into the egg. You need enough salt to fill about one-third of the egg.

4. Seal the second hole and your egg is finished.

Now you can balance your egg in some very interesting positions, because, whichever way you position the egg, the salt runs to the bottom and acts as a weight to hold it at whatever angle you like!

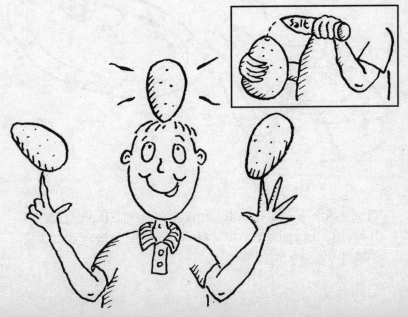

IN A SPIN

Here's an amazing feat of juggling you can perform with just a flat-rimmed plate and a piece of egg shell.

1. Cut the top off a boiled egg. Eat the egg but keep the end of the shell you have cut off.

2. Wet the plate with water. Put the half-shell on the edge of the plate and then tilt the plate a little.

3. The shell will begin to slide down the plate but it will spin as it does so.

This trick looks really amazing, and if you keep turning the plate you can keep the shell moving for quite a long time.

ANIMATED EGG

Ask your friends to gather round and watch, as you place an egg on the table. When you wave your hands mysteriously over the egg it will roll along the table of its own accord!

This trick looks like magic, but it's really very easy to do. The waving of the hands is just to draw everyone's attention away from the fact that you are blowing on the egg!

One thing you mustn't tell your audience is that the egg has been blown (see page 52) to make it lighter!

Remember to practise this trick a few times before you let anyone watch.

Did you know...?

The furthest an egg has been thrown without it breaking is 96.90 m (317 feet 10 in)!

STRAW EGGS

Every time you have a boiled egg keep the shell. You can then use them for this party game.

1. The players are divided into two teams. Each team is given half an eggshell and each player has a drinking straw.

2. The teams stand in two lines holding the straws in their mouths.

3. When the game starts, the first player in the team puts the eggshell on top of the straw in her mouth.

4. She then turns to the next player in the line and the second player tries to lift the shell onto his straw.

5. The first team to get the shell all the way along the line like this wins.

6. The players must not touch the shell once the game has started. If anyone touches the shell, that team has to start again.

It's a good idea to have a few spare shells handy just in case some are broken.

EGG BLOW

This is a riotous game for two people. All you need is a clean, blown egg. Put the egg on a table between yourself and your friend.

Now, both of you blow as hard as you can! Try to blow the egg off the other person's side of the table.

Score each time this happens.

EGG FLIP

Tell a friend that you can put an egg on the floor so that she can't jump over it.

Put the egg in a corner of the room. She can't jump over it there!

EGG AND SPOON RACE

Here's a very old game that's still great fun to play!

1. Give each player a dessertspoon and an egg.

2. Ask everyone to place their egg on the spoon.

3. Ask someone to give starting orders and the race begins!

The winner is the first person to reach the winning post without dropping the egg.

Note: Glueing the egg to the spoon is definitely not allowed!

Did you know...?

The fastest anyone has completed an egg and spoon marathon of 45.86 km (28.5 miles) is 4 hours and 34 minutes.

THE UNTOUCHABLE EGG

Show your friend an egg and tell him that if he can pick it up from a piece of newspaper he is standing on, you'll give him a prize. If he can't, he'll have to give you a prize.

It sounds quite easy and it's very likely that your friend will take you up on this.

You then put the newspaper on the floor in an open doorway. Place the egg on the paper then close the door.

Now ask your friend to stand on the paper. He can't pick up the egg because the door is in the way, so you claim your prize!

AMAZING EGG DROP

This trick looks incredibly skilful, but it's really quite easy to do. You do need some practice to get it right, though. It's best to practise in a garden – for obvious reasons!

1. Fill four plastic cups with water and place them on the ground.

2. Put a square tray on top of the cups. Try to use a tray that has a slightly raised edge all round.

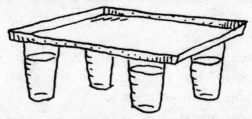

3. Next, roll up four playing cards into tubes. Hold them in place with elastic bands.

4. Place each tube on the tray immediately over the tops of the cups.

5. Now balance an egg on the top of each tube and you are ready to perform this amazing trick.

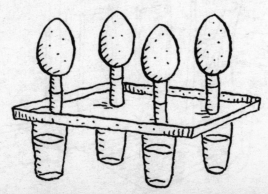

6. Give the tray a sharp blow on one edge. This knocks the tray and the tubes away and the eggs drop down into the plastic cups of water!

What? It didn't work? Well, you obviously need some more practice!

The real secrets of this trick are to have the confidence to do it and to give the tray a quick sharp blow.

Keep trying – you'll get it right eventually.

WALKING ON EGGS

This is a great party trick.

1. Lay several eggs in a line on the floor.

2. Ask one of your party guests to walk from one side of the room to the other, stepping over the eggs as she goes. Tell her to remember where each egg is.

3. Now challenge her to do it blindfold! Cover her eyes with a large scarf. Take your time, and while you are doing this get one of your friends, who is in on the joke, to quickly pick up all the eggs.

4. Now let your victim walk across the room, thinking she's about to crush an egg all over the carpet! It's not much fun for her, but the rest of your friends will be helpless with laughter!

CRACKED SHELLS

Try this version of the same trick on a smooth floor that can be wiped clean only! The kitchen floor is probably best.

This time, take away the eggs as usual, but replace them with prawn crackers.

When your next victim treads on a prawn cracker he'll think he has trodden on an egg!

Make sure you clean up quickly, afterwards.

Did you know...?
People once believed that witches sailed out to sea in egg shells! They would follow the fishing fleets and use their magical powers to sink the boats.

KEEP ON SPINNING

1. Place a raw egg on its side and give it a good hard spin.

2. Stop it spinning by suddenly placing your finger on top of it.

3. Lift your finger and the egg will start spinning again!

This works because the contents of the egg are spinning around inside the shell. When you stop the shell, the contents continue to spin. Let go and the egg will move again.

Don't stop the egg for too long or this trick won't work.

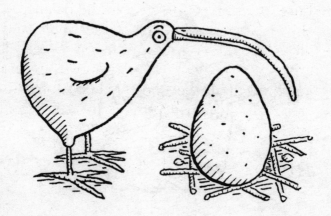

Did you know...?

The kiwi lays the largest egg in proportion to its own size. The egg is about one-fifth the size of the bird that laid it.

WHAT A CORKER!

1. Show your friends an empty bottle and a hard-boiled egg. Challenge someone to balance the egg on the rim of the bottle.

2. Anyone who tries is bound to fail, so it's a good idea to have several hard-boiled eggs handy. (You can always make some egg sandwiches or an egg salad for your friends afterwards).

3. When several people have tried and failed you show them how it is done. All you have to do is push two dinner forks into each side of a cork (you very conveniently forgot to tell your friends that they could use other objects to help in the balance).

4. Hold the egg on the rim of the bottle and then carefully place the cork and forks on top (as shown in the picture). You may have to move the egg, the cork or the forks to get the right position, but it is now quite easy to balance the egg on the bottle as shown.

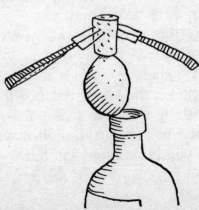

THE GREAT EGGSPLORER

According to an old story the great explorer, Christopher Columbus, was once challenged to stand an egg on end. He solved the problem by banging the egg on the table so hard that the bottom of the shell cracked and the egg remained standing.

There are, however, two possible ways to stand an egg on end without breaking it.

1. The first is to shake the egg as hard as you can. This breaks the yolk inside the egg, so it is possible to stand the egg on its broad end.

Unfortunately, this doesn't work every time so you'll have to practise.

2. Alternatively, when no-one is looking, pour a small pile of salt on the table. Balance the egg on the salt by pushing down to make a sort of nest. Now blow the salt away! Although it will not be visible, there will be enough salt left to keep the egg upright.

Show the egg to your friends and then hand it to someone and ask them to do the same thing. Wipe away any traces of salt while you are holding it, and no-one will be able to work out how the trick is done.

MISERABLE EGG

When you shout at an egg it begins to cry!

1. Hide a piece of wet tissue in the fingers of your left hand.

2. With your right hand show a hard-boiled egg.

3. Start shouting at the egg as you place it into your left hand (on top of the tissue).

4. If you now squeeze the tissue against the egg, water will drip from it and the egg will look as if it is crying.

EGG HUNT

An egg hunt is a traditional game for all the family to join in at Easter.

1. First you need to hard-boil some eggs – at least one for each member of the family.

2. When the eggs have cooled and dried, you can decorate them as described on pp 50, 54 and 56.

3. Early on Easter Sunday, hide the eggs all over the house even in the garden if it's fine. Think hard about where to hide them – try to find some unusual hiding places. Then gather the family in one room and send them out to search for the eggs – they all have to run around the house as fast as they can to find as many eggs as possible.

You could organize a prize for whoever collects the most eggs, but don't let them eat everything they find – you still need an egg for everybody.

You could do this with chocolate eggs too.

DISAPPEARING EGG

The easiest way to make an egg disappear
is to eat it. But you can also do it by magic.
You'll need a hard-boiled egg and a friend to
help.
1. Show the egg on your hand.
2. Cover it with a handkerchief and go to each of
your friends in turn asking them to feel under the
handkerchief to make sure the egg is still there.
3. After everyone has felt the egg, whip the
handkerchief away – and the egg has disappeared!

4. What happens is that the last person who feels
under the handkerchief is your secret assistant.
5. He doesn't feel the egg – he secretly takes it
away.
6. All you now have to do is act like a mysterious
magician and pretend you have made the egg
vanish.

EGG ON AIR

With your amazing magical powers, you can make an egg float on air! (What your friends don't see is that the egg is really balanced on a loop of thread held between your hands!)

1. Before your performance, secretly make the loop of thread and place it on a table. Rest a hard-boiled egg on the thread near the centre as shown in the picture.

2. Now put your thumbs in each end of the loop and lift your hands with the loop taut between them. It takes a bit of practice to keep the egg balanced on the cotton loop, but it can look really impressive!

It's a good idea to keep a reasonable distance away from your audience when you do this trick, so the thread is less likely to be noticed. Use dark thread, too, and make sure you wear dark clothes to hide the thread even more.

EGG IN A BOTTLE

Did you know that it is possible to push a chicken's egg into a narrow-necked bottle?
This is how you do it:

1. Boil the egg for about ten minutes, until it is really hard-boiled.

2. Allow the egg to cool.

3. Soak the boiled egg in vinegar for about a day.

4. Put an empty milk bottle into a bowl of hot water for about five minutes. Be careful that it isn't too hot – you don't want to scald yourself or break the bottle.

5. Put the egg on the neck of the bottle and push it gently. The vinegar will have softened the shell and the egg should go into the bottle quite easily.

EGG CONTROL

Your audience will be amazed when you place an egg on a table and it rolls along at your command! And as soon as you tell it to stop it stops.

Any of your friends watching can examine the egg, but they'll find it's just an ordinary hard-boiled egg.

What your friends don't know is that you have a secret assistant in the room who helped you with the trick.

1. Before showing the trick, put a plastic ring on the table (under the tablecloth). Attached to this ring is a long length of cotton. Your secret assistant knows all about this.

2. When you show the trick, your friend sits at the table by the end of the cotton. The egg is shown and put on the table – on top of the plastic ring, hidden under the cloth.

3. At your command, your friend pulls the secret cotton, which pulls the ring, and the egg seems to be rolling across the table by itself! As soon as you say "stop", your friend stops pulling the cotton and the egg stops rolling.

4. You then pick up the egg and hand it to a spectator for examination. While your friends are looking at it, your friend can quickly pull the ring from under the tablecloth without being seen.

Did you know...?

Dick Williams, of Penryn in Cornwall, was a well-known strong man. He claimed his strength came from eating six raw eggs and drinking a litre (2 pints) of milk each day. Mr Williams could lift a 136 kg (300 lb) dumb-bell which held a 87 kg (12 stone) man who in turn held two 13.5 kg (30 lb) dumb-bells!

FRIED OR BOILED?

Tell your friends you like eggs so much, that you can tell the difference between boiled eggs and fried eggs even when the eggs don't exist! This sounds a crazy boast, but you can prove it with this trick.

1. Write the words "boiled" and "fried" on a sheet of card, as shown in the picture, and tear the card into nine pieces.

2. Drop the pieces into a paper bag or box. Shake them up so they are well mixed.

3. Reach into the bag and take a piece of card. Before looking at the card, or showing it to anyone, say whether it says "boiled" or "fried".

4. The secret is in the way the different words are positioned on the card before it is torn.

Look at the picture and you will see that all "fried" pieces have only one straight edge. The "boiled" pieces have two straight edges, except that one piece has no straight edges whatsoever.

When you take a piece of card from the bag you can easily feel the edges with your fingertips and know instantly whether or not it says "boiled" or "fried".

Did you know...?

The ancient Persians and Egyptians believed that the world was hatched from an egg on the first day of spring. Each spring they gave one another presents of red and blue dyed eggs in celebration.

LEMON EGG

Here is a really amazing magic trick you can perform quite easily.

Show a lemon which you cover with a handkerchief. When you whisk the handkerchief away, the lemon has turned into an egg!

This trick needs some secret preparation before you can show it.

1. You will need a lemon that is a little bigger than the egg you plan to use. Carefully cut the peel open and use a knife and spoon to scoop out the fruit.

2. Allow the peel to dry out and then put a hard-boiled egg inside it.

3. Hold the peel closed and it looks as if it is an ordinary lemon.

4. Cover the lemon with a handkerchief, say a few magic words and then remove the handkerchief. At the same time taking the lemon peel off the egg.

5. Keep the peel hidden in the handkerchief as you show the egg.

6. Put the handkerchief (with the lemon peel still hidden in it) into your pocket, as you show the egg.

It looks as if this trick is really magic!

Did you know...?

The ostrich lays the largest egg of any bird. It can be up to 20 cm (8 in) high, with a diameter of up to 15 cm (6 in) and weighs anything up to 1.78 kg (3.88 lbs).

Did you know...?

The Vervain hummingbird, from Jamaica, lays the smallest bird's egg. It can be as small as 10 mm (0.39 in) long and weigh as little as 0.365 g (0.128 oz).

What's white and yellow and zooms along the motorway at 70 miles per hour?
A lorry driver's egg sandwich.

How can you find out about eggs?
Consult an hencyclopedia.

What do you call someone who knows all there is to know about eggs?
An eggspert.

Where do athletic hens compete?
At the Olympegg Games.

What did the matador say at breakfast?
Scram bull.

What do scientists do with eggs?
Eggsperiment.

What brand of petrol do eggs put in their cars?
Shell.

89

What did the Spanish farmer say to his hens?
Oh-lay.

What do you call a policeman who searches for missing hens?
A deteggtive.

What sort of trains do eggs travel on?
Eggspress trains.

Knock, knock.
Who's there?
Eggbert.
Eggbert who?
Eggbert no bacon.

What do you call a monk who cooks eggs and bacon?
A friar

1st egg in saucepan: "Phew it's hot in here!"
2nd egg: "This is nothing. When you get out, they're going to bash your head in and scoop out your insides!"

How many boiled eggs can you eat on an empty stomach?
One – then your stomach isn't empty any more.

What goes up brown and comes down yellow and white?
An egg.

How do gamekeepers like their eggs?
Poached.

How do kangaroos like their eggs?
Pouched.

Nicola: Did you hear about the three eggs?
Nicholas: No
Nicola: Two bad!

What did the egg say to the whisk?
I know when I'm beaten.

What is an egg's favourite play?
Omelette.

What do you call a silly chick?
A comedi–hen.

What do you get if you cross the white of an egg
with a pound of gunpowder?
A boom-meringue.

Knock, knock.
Who's there?
Marmalade
Marmalade who?
Marmalade me a little egg.

Doctor: I'm afraid you've only got three minutes left to live.

Patient: Is there nothing you can do for me?

Doctor: I could boil you an egg.

"Waiter, waiter, this egg smells bad!"
"Don't blame me, madam. I only laid the table."

Which is the best day for cooking eggs and bacon?
Fryday.

What happens if you play table-tennis with a rotten egg?
First it goes ping and then it goes pong.

How do ghosts like their eggs?
Terrifried!

Who is the chicken's favourite author?
Charles Chickens – author of Great Eggspectations!